Contents

Stop Chatting, Bill 3

Queen Anneena's Feast 21

Spike Says 39

The Wrong Kind of Knight 57

Moan, Moan, Moan! 75

The Snake and the Drake ... 93

Tadpoles 111

OXFORD
UNIVERSITY PRESS

Great Clarendon Street, Oxford, OX2 6DP, United Kingdom

Oxford University Press is a department of the University
of Oxford. It furthers the University's objective of excellence
in research, scholarship, and education by publishing
worldwide. Oxford is a registered trade mark of Oxford
University Press in the UK and in certain other countries

British Library Cataloguing in Publication Data
Data available

ISBN: 978-0-19-276480-5

10 9 8 7 6 5 4 3 2 1

Paper used in the production of this book is a natural, recyclable product
made from wood grown in sustainable forests. The manufacturing process
conforms to the environmental regulations of the country of origin.

Printed in China

Acknowledgements

Series Editor: Clare Kirtley

Cover illustration by Teresa Murfin

The Wrong Kind of Knight illustrated by Melanie Williamson

Moan, Moan, Moan! illustrated by Barbara Vagnozzi

Tadpoles illustrated by Susie Thomas

Stop Chatting, Bill

Tips for reading Stop Chatting, Bill together

This story practises this letter pattern:

oo

Ask your child to point to this letter pattern and say the sound (*oo* as in *too*). Look out for this letter pattern in the story.

Your child might find these words tricky:

the   to   of   go   come   says   what   you
school   she   he   like   my   said

These words are common, but your child may not be able to sound them out yet. Say the words for your child if they do not know them.

Before you begin, ask your child to read the title by sounding out first (say each sound out loud, e.g. *st-o-p*) and then blending the word together (e.g. *stop*). Look at the picture together. What do you think this story is about?

Remind your child to read unfamiliar words by saying the individual sounds separately and then blending them together quickly to read the word. When you have finished reading the story, look through it again and:

- Ask your child, *Why didn't Bill tell everyone about his tooth?* (Miss Hill had told him to stop chatting.)
- Point to the letter pattern that makes the long vowel sound in *smooth*. Say what sound this letter pattern makes (*oo* as in *moon*). Find and read some more words in the story that contain the letter pattern *oo* (*school, too, tooth*).

"Come and sit on the mat," says
Miss Hill.

"What did you bring to school, Flick?" says Miss Hill.
Flick has a magnet. "It can pick up pins," she says.

The pins stick to the magnet. The magnet picks up lots of clips too. The children clap.

But Bill is not clapping. He is chatting to Fred.

"Stop chatting to Fred," says
Miss Hill.
"Go and sit next to Jess."

"What did you bring to school, Fred?"
says Miss Hill.
Fred has a box of shells.

"I like this smooth pink shell best," he says. The children clap.

But Bill is not clapping. He is chatting to Jess.

"Stop chatting to Jess," says Miss Hill. "Go and sit next to the fish tank."

"What did you bring in, Jess?"
says Miss Hill.
"This is my pet stick insect," says Jess.
"It can lift
its left leg."

The stick insect lifts its leg.
The children clap.

But Bill is not clapping. He is chatting to the fish!

"Stop chatting to the fish, Bill," says Miss Hill. "What did you bring in?"

Bill stands up. He has a tooth in his hand.
"Well?" says Miss Hill.
But Bill just stands still.

"Go on," says Miss Hill. "Tell us about the tooth."

"But Miss," says Bill. "You said I had to stop chatting."

Queen Anneena's Feast

Tips for reading Queen Anneena's Feast together

This story practises these letter patterns that all make the same sound:

ee ea y e

Ask your child to point to these letter patterns and say the sound
(e.g. *ee* as in *Queen*). Look out for these letter patterns in the story.

Your child might find these words tricky:

to the you no was came going
have home some said are our

These words are common, but your child may not be able to sound them
out yet. Say the words for your child if they do not know them.

Before you begin, ask your child to read the title by sounding out first
(say each sound out loud, e.g. *Qu-ee-n*) and then blending the word
together (e.g. *Queen*). Look at the picture together. What do you think
this story is about?

When you have finished reading the story, look through it again and:

- Ask your child, *What were the queens going to do when they got home?*
  (Brush their teeth.) *Why is it important to brush your teeth?* (To keep
  teeth clean and healthy.)
- On page 38, find and read some words that contain a long *ee* sound
  (*we, clean, teeth*). Point to the letter pattern that makes the long *ee*
  sound in the words. Think of other words that contain long *ee* sounds
  (e.g. *she, he, leaf, dream, feet, tree*).

Queen Anneena had a feast.

Fifteen queens came to the feast.

The queens sat on sixteen green seats.

Queen Jean had heaps of meat.

Queen Betty had heaps of curry.

Queen Poppy had heaps of peas and beans.

Queen Nelly had eels with seaweed!

The queens drank lots of tea and coffee.

Queen Anneena was very happy to see the queens eat and drink.

"Will you have some peaches and cream?" she said.

"No," said the fifteen queens.

"Will you have some jelly?" said Queen Anneena.

"No," said the queens.

"Will you have some sweets and toffees?"

"No," said the queens.

"We are going home to clean our teeth."

Spike Says

Tips for reading Spike Says together

This story practises these letter patterns that all make the same sound:

igh   y   ie   i–e   i

Ask your child to point to these letter patterns and say the sound (*i–e* as in *Spike*). Look out for these letter patterns in the story.

Your child might find these words tricky:

my   no   the   to   you   was   came
do   going   have   home   one
some   said   there   want   what

These words are common, but your child may not be able to sound them out yet. Say the words for your child if they do not know them.

Before you begin, ask your child to read the title by sounding out first (say each sound out loud, e.g. *Sp-i-k-e*) and then blending the word together (e.g. *Spike*). Look at the picture together. What do you think this story is about?

When you have finished reading the story, look through it again and:

- Ask your child, *Which of Spike's claims do you like best? Why?*
- Find and read some words on pages 55 and 56 that contain a long *ie* sound (*pie, sky, night, Spike, lie*). Point to the letter pattern that makes the long *ie* sound in the word (*ie, y, igh, i–consonant–e, ie*). Think of other words that contain the long *ie* sound (e.g. *light, my, cry, like*).

Spike is five.

Spike says he can run for miles

and miles.

Spike says he has nine bikes.

45

Spike says he can dive.

He says he wins prizes for diving.

Spike says he can drive.

He says he wins prizes for driving.

Spike says he can fight fires

and feed wild lions.

Spike says his mum is a spy

and his dad rides a crocodile.

Spike says he can fly.

He says he eats a pie in the sky every night.

Spike says that he never, ever tells a lie.

The Wrong Kind of Knight

Tips for reading The Wrong Kind of Knight together

This story practises these letter patterns:

> ee   ea   e   y   (all pronounced *ee* as in *three*)
>
> ie   i-e   igh   i   y   (all pronounced *ie* as in *tie*)
>
> n   kn   (pronounced *n* as in *not*)
>
> r   wr   (pronounced *r* as in *ran*)

Ask your child to point to these letter patterns and say the sounds
(e.g. *n* as in *not*). Look out for these letter patterns in the story.

Your child might find these words tricky:

> the   to   too   you   no   was   never   knickers   don't
>
> door   liked   one   said   saw   some   there   were

These words are common, but your child may not be able to sound them
out yet. Say the words for your child if they do not know them.

Before you begin, ask your child to read the title by sounding out first
(say each sound out loud, e.g. *wr-o-ng*) and then blending the word together
(e.g. *wrong*). Look at the picture together. What do you think this story is about?

When you have finished reading the story, look through it again and:

- Ask your child, *Was Nasim the wrong kind of knight? Why?* (No, because he
  got rid of the dragon.)
- Find and read some words on page 71 that begin with an *n* sound
  (*no, knight, Nasim, knit*). Point to the letter patterns that make the *n* sound
  (*n, kn*).

Nasim was a knight.

But he didn't like to ride and he didn't like to fight.

Nasim liked to read and write, and he liked to knit.

One night, there was a knock at the door.

"I need you to fight a dragon!"
cried King Kareem.

"But I'm the wrong kind of knight!" said Nasim. "I don't like fighting!"

"Never mind!" cried the king.
"Hurry up!"

"The dragon is in my bed!" said the king.

Nasim's knees were knocking.
He lifted the blanket and saw . . .

a tiny dragon.

The dragon's knees were
knocking too.
"I'm freezing," he said.

"Fight him!" cried the king.

"No. I'm the wrong kind of knight," said Nasim, and he began to knit.

Nasim was very quick at knitting.
He knitted a vest, some socks and
some long knickers.

The dragon was delighted.
"Thank you!" he said, and off
he went.

"I think you were the right kind of knight!" said the king.

Moan, Moan, Moan!

Tips for reading Moan, Moan, Moan! together

This story practises these letter patterns that all make the same sound:

oa ow o–e o

Ask your child to point to these letter patterns and say the sound (*oa* as in *moan*). Look out for these letter patterns in the story.

Your child might find these words tricky:

climb   come   never   says   sister's
thumb   to   was   you   your

These words are common, but your child may not be able to sound them out yet. Say the words for your child if they do not know them.

Before you begin, ask your child to read the title by sounding out first (say each sound out loud, e.g. *m-oa-n*) and then blending the word together (e.g. *moan*). Look at the picture together. What do you think this story is about?

When you have finished reading the story, look through it again and:

- Ask your child, *Why did the child wish her goldfish was her mum?* (Because her goldfish never moans.)

- Read pages 78 and 79, and find some words that contain a long *oe* sound (*don't, throw, stones, moans*). Point to the letter pattern that makes the long *oe* sound in the words (*o, ow, o–consonant–e, oa*). Find and read some more words that contain the letter pattern *oa* (*coat, soap, coal, slowcoach, toast, road*).

My goldfish never moans at me.
She never says,
"Don't climb that tree."

She never tells me,
"Don't throw stones."

But Mum just moans and moans and moans.

81

82

84

85

87

89

I wish my goldfish was my mum.

The Snake and the Drake

Tips for reading The Snake and the Drake together

This story practises these letter patterns that all make the same sound:

ai   ay   a–e   a

Ask your child to point to these letter patterns and say the sound (*ai* as in *rainy*). Look out for these letter patterns in the story.

Your child might find these words tricky:

can't   come   every   one   the   to
said   some   what   you

These words are common, but your child may not be able to sound them out yet. Say the words for your child if they do not know them.

Before you begin, ask your child to read the title by sounding out first (say each sound out loud, e.g. *sn-a-k-e*) and then blending the word together (e.g. *snake*). Look at the picture together. What do you think this story is about?

When you have finished reading the story, look through it again and:

- Ask your child, *Why did the snake let the drake get away?* (He thought the drake would bring him some yummy cake.)
- Read page 96, find some words that contain a long *ai* sound (*rainy, day, a, snake, came*). Point to the letter pattern that makes the long *ai* sound in the words (*ai, ay, a, a–consonant–e*). Find and read some more words that contain the letter pattern *ay* (*away, way, okay, lay*).

A duck and a drake had a nest
by a lake.

One rainy day, a snake came to the nest.

The duck got away but the snake got the drake.

"Let go of my tail," said the drake.
"No," said the snake. "I am going to eat you."

"Will you eat me with some cake?" said the drake. "That is the best way to eat drake."

"I can't make cake," said the snake.

"But Raven can make cake," said the drake.

"Raven's cake is yummy," said the drake.

102

"He makes it every day."

"What is in Raven's cake?" said
the snake.

"Grapes and dates and raisins," said the drake.

"Yum yum," said the snake. "What a shame I can't fly to Raven's nest."

"But I can fly," said the drake.
"If you wait, I can get you some
of Raven's yummy cake."

"Okay. I will wait," said the snake, and he let the drake get away.

Snake lay and waited. He waited all day. But the drake did not come back.

Snake is still waiting.

Tadpoles

Tips for reading Tadpoles together

This story practises these letter patterns:

ee ea y e (all pronounced *ee* as in *three*)
i—e i (pronounced *ie* as in *tie*)
ow o—e o (all pronounced *oe* as in *toe*)
ai ay a—e a (all pronounced *ai* as in *train*)

Ask your child to point to these letter patterns and say the sounds
(e.g. *ee* as in *three*). Look out for these letter patterns in the story.

Your child might find these words tricky:

all are comes have here out some
these they the to what you

These words are common, but your child may not be able to sound them
out yet. Say the words for your child if they do not know them.

Before you begin, ask your child to read the title by sounding out first
(say each sound out loud, e.g. *j-e-ll-y*) and then blending the word together
(e.g. *jelly*). Look at the picture together. What do you think this story is about?

When you have finished reading the story, look through it again and:

- Ask your child, *How does the tadpole change as it turns into a frog?* (It
  grows back legs, then front legs. It loses its tail.)
- Find and read some more words on page 115 that contain a long vowel
  sound (*grow, jelly*). Point to the letter pattern that makes the long vowel
  sound in these words (*ow, y*). Find and read some more words that
  contain a long *oe* sound (*those, growing, tadpoles, tadpole, only, no*).

What can you see in this lake?
Can you see some blobs of jelly?

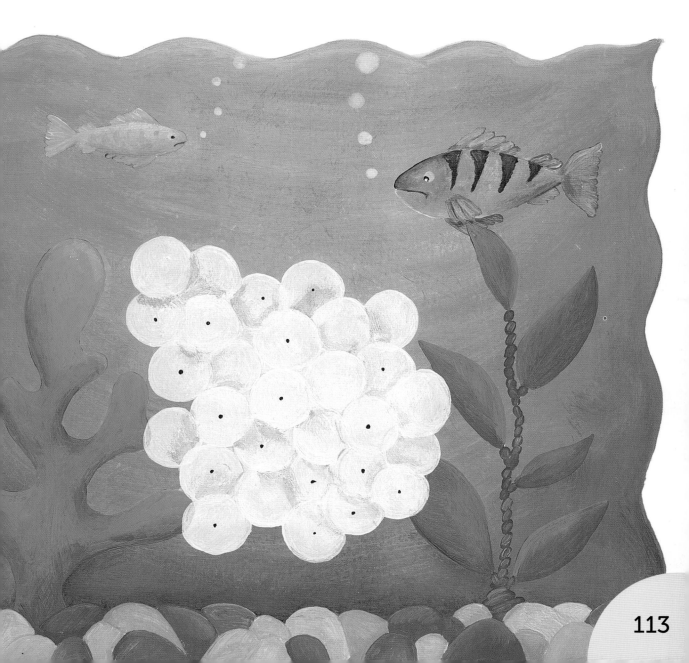

Can you see some black dots inside the jelly? Those dots are tiny eggs.

The dots grow. The jelly shrinks.

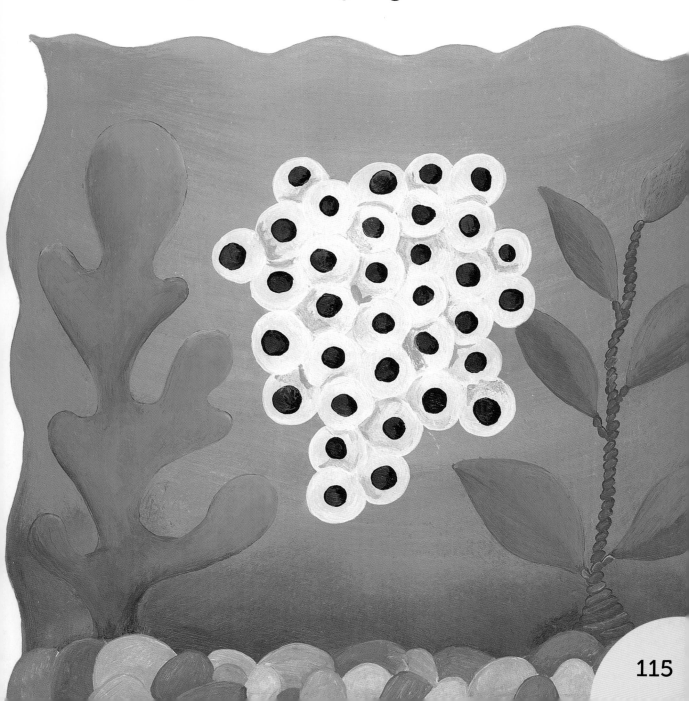

The dots are growing tails. They are baby tadpoles!

The tadpoles are tiny. They stick to the weeds.

Then they begin to swim.

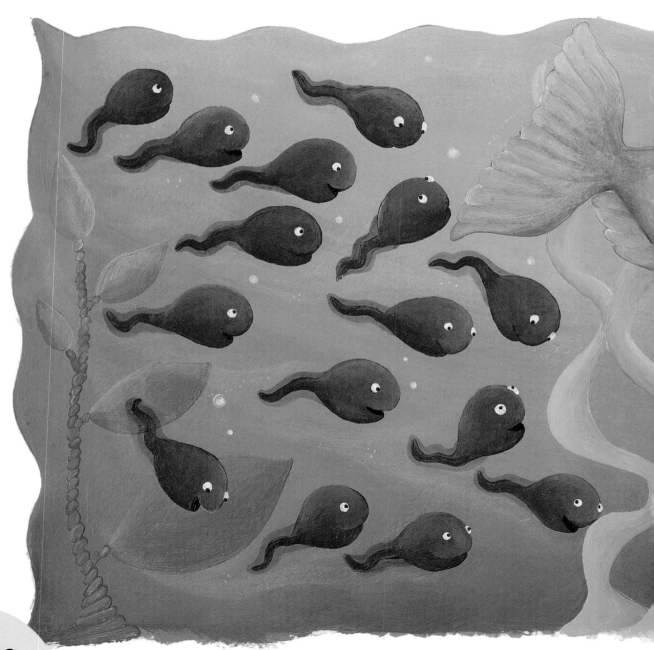

Quick, tadpoles, swim away!
Here comes a big fish!

The fish eats some of the tadpoles.

The rest swim away. They hide in the weeds.

Can you see some bumps on this tadpole? Those bumps will be legs.

These tadpoles only have
back legs.

This tadpole has all its legs.
Its tail is shrinking.

This tadpole has no tail.

The tadpole kicks with its legs.
It jumps out of the lake.

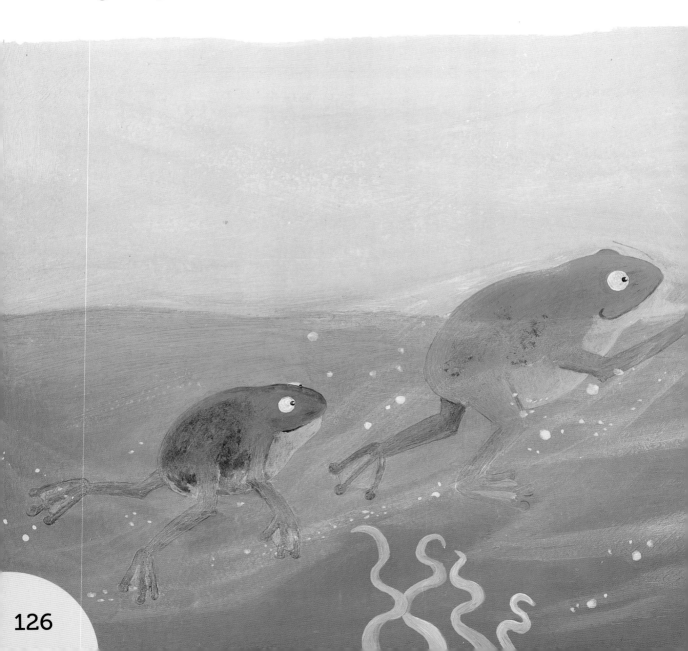

But is it a tadpole?

No, it's a frog!